The Afternoon Pianist

This publication is not authorised for sale in the
United States of America and/or Canada.

Wise Publications
part of The Music Sales Group

London/New York/Sydney/Paris/Copenhagen/Madrid/Tokyo

Published by
Wise Publications
8/9 Frith Street, London W1D 3JB, England.

Exclusive distributors:
Music Sales Limited
Distribution Centre, Newmarket Road,
Bury St Edmunds, Suffolk IP33 3YB, England.
Music Sales Pty Limited
120 Rothschild Avenue, Rosebery, NSW 2018, Australia.

Order No. AM977141
ISBN 1-84449-027-0
This book © Copyright 2003 by Wise Publications

Music arranged by Derek Jones.
Music processed by Enigma Music Production Services.
Compiled, written & edited by Sarah Holcroft.
Cover photograph courtesy of Images Colour Library.
All other photographs courtesy of London Features International,
Ronald Grant Archive and The Really Useful Group Ltd.

Printed in the United Kingdom by
Thanet Press Limited, Margate, Kent.

www.musicsales.com

Your Guarantee of Quality
As publishers, we strive to produce every book to the highest
commercial standards. The music has been freshly engraved and
the book has been carefully designed to minimise awkward page
turns and to make playing from it a real pleasure. Particular care has
been given to specifying acid-free, neutral-sized paper made from
pulps which have not been elemental chlorine bleached. This pulp
is from farmed sustainable forests and was produced with special
regard for the environment. Throughout, the printing and binding
have been planned to ensure a sturdy, attractive publication which
should give years of enjoyment. If your copy fails to meet our high
standards, please inform us and we will gladly replace it.

Foreword

The Afternoon Pianist has been specially designed to cater for the less experienced adult learner.

This larger-print compilation features well-known songs from 20th Century musical theatre, as well as pictures and a short commentary on each show.

The titles have been arranged in order of difficulty, allowing you to work your way through the collection learning new techniques, keys and time signatures.

A glossary has been provided as a quick reference to any unknown musical terms and symbols.

Each piece is accompanied by a short tutorial which offers guidance on how to tackle the more difficult aspects of the music. Fingerings and chord diagrams are provided throughout.

Learning a piece of music takes time and dedication. We hope that our tips will help to make learning easier, so that you can really enjoy playing the music in this collection.

CAROUSEL (1945)

You'll Never Walk Alone

Words & Music by Richard Rodgers & Oscar Hammerstein II

Based upon Liliom, a play by Ferenc Molnar, Carousel opened at the Majestic Theatre, New York in 1945. In 1956 a film version was made starring Gordon McRae as central character Billy Bigelow. The story tells of good-for-nothing Billy, who is killed during a failed robbery. At the gates of heaven he is given one chance to redeem himself by returning to earth to brighten the life of his 15-year old daughter. His parting message to her is contained in this, the final song; 'You'll Never Walk Alone'.

Use these chord diagrams as a guide to help you find your way around the keyboard:

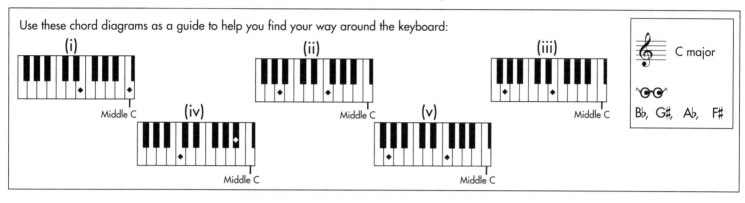

With warmth, like a hymn

When you

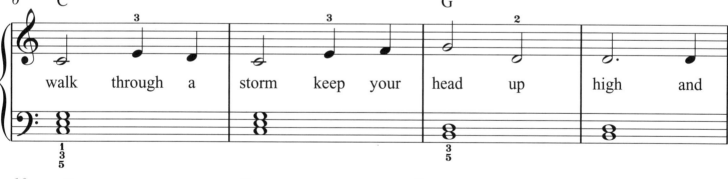

walk through a storm keep your head up high and

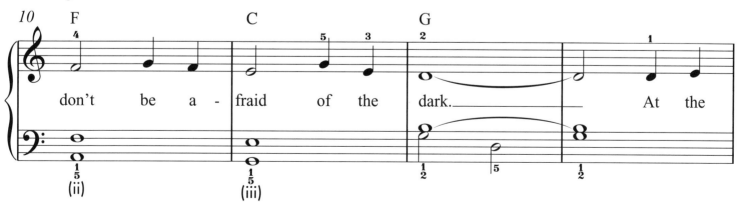

don't be a - fraid of the dark. At the

6

SOUTH PACIFIC (1949)

Younger Than Springtime

Words & Music by Oscar Hammerstein II & Richard Rodgers

Based on James A. Michener's Tales Of The South Pacific, Rodgers and Hammerstein's stage show South Pacific is a love story set amidst the conflict between American and Japanese troops in World War II. Packed with classic tunes such as 'There Is Nothing Like A Dame', 'Happy Talking', 'I'm Gonna Wash That Man Right Outa My Hair' and 'Some Enchanted Evening' the show is still hugely popular. In 1958 the musical was released as a movie starring Mitzi Gaynor and Rosanno Brazzi (pictured here).

Follow the fingering suggestions provided to make learning this piece as easy as possible.

Use these chord diagrams as a guide:

C major

F#

(i) Middle C   (ii) Middle C   (iii) Middle C   (iv) Middle C

Moderately

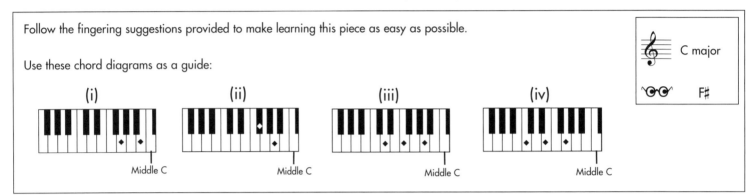

Young-er than spring-time   are you,   soft-er than star-light

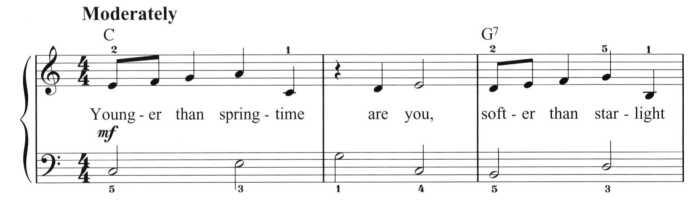

are you,   warm-er than winds of   June are the gen-tle   lips you

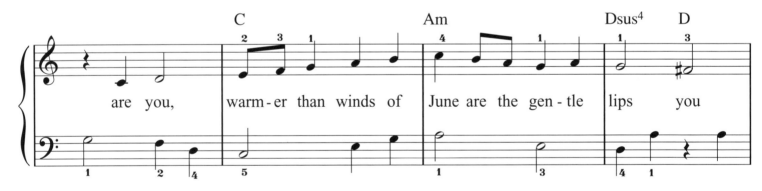

gave me.   Gay-er than laugh-ter   are you,   sweet-er than mu-sic   are you.

9

SHOWBOAT (1927)

Ol' Man River

Words & Music by Jerome Kern & Oscar Hammerstein II

Based on the novel by Edna Ferber, Hammerstein & Kern's Showboat spans four decades to tell the story of the Cotton Blossom Floating Theatre, the Hawkes family and their show boat troupe of actors. Set in one of the most dramatic eras of American history, the musical paints a portrait of the ugliness of racism, marital discord and abandonment. The show contains some of the most popular tunes in the history of American musical theatre.

Use these chord diagrams as a guide to help you with the more tricky 7th stretches in this piece:

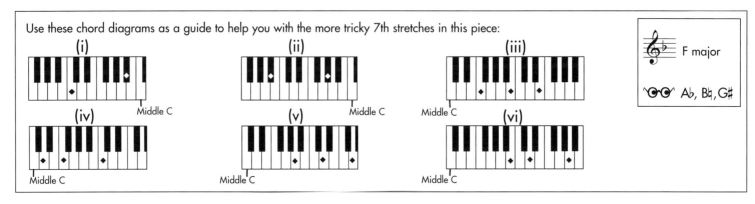

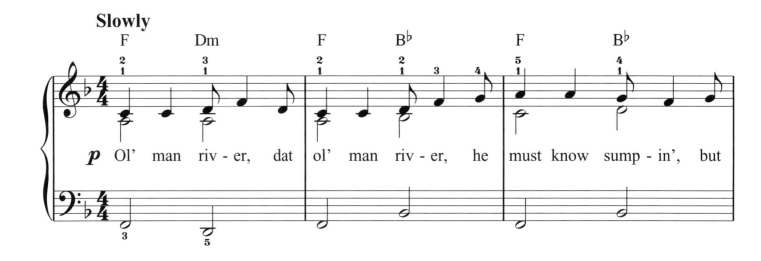

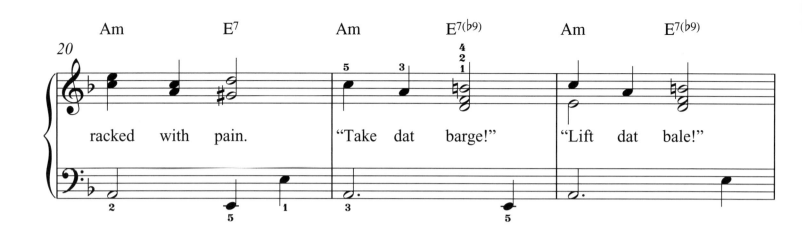

racked with pain. "Take dat barge!" "Lift dat bale!"

rit.   **a tempo**

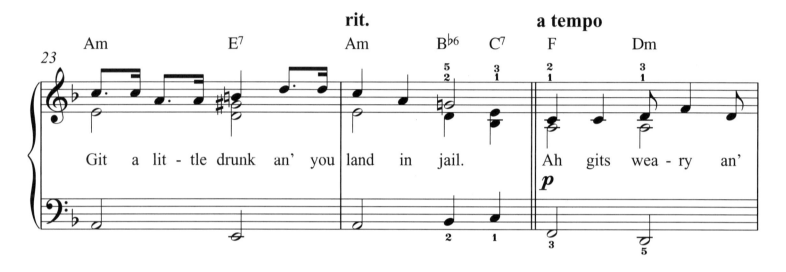

Git a lit-tle drunk an' you land in jail. Ah gits wea-ry an'

p

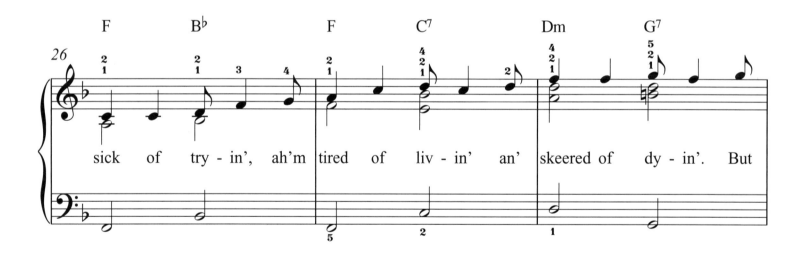

sick of try-in', ah'm tired of liv-in' an' skeered of dy-in'. But

rit.

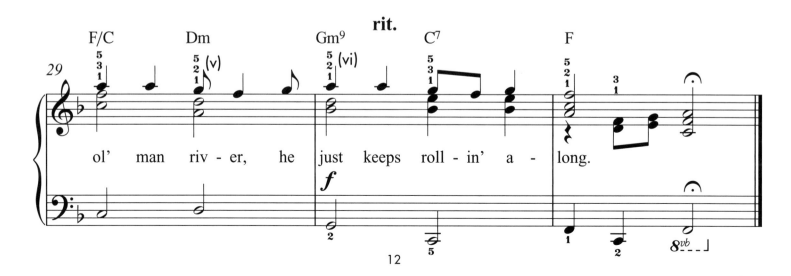

ol' man riv-er, he just keeps roll-in' a - long.

f

OLIVER! (1960)

As Long As He Needs Me

Words & Music by Lionel Bart

Based on Charles Dickens' classic novel Oliver Twist, Lionel Bart's musical Oliver! opened in London's West End in 1960. Eight years later Carol Reed directed a film version with a host of stars including Mark Lester as Oliver Twist (pictured here), Jack Wild as The Artful Dodger, Oliver Reed as Bill Sykes, Harry Seycombe as Mr. Bumble and the unforgetteable Ron Moody as Fagen. 'As Long As He Needs Me' is just one of the show's memorable titles, sung by the character Nancy.

In the final bars of this piece the 5th finger of the right hand acts as an anchor, i.e. it is held down while the second voice is played beneath.

Following the fingering suggestions provided, practise the second voice part on its own.

Then try adding the 5th finger above.

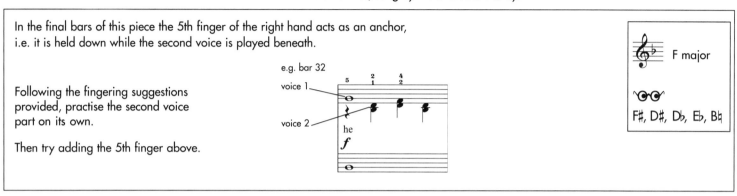

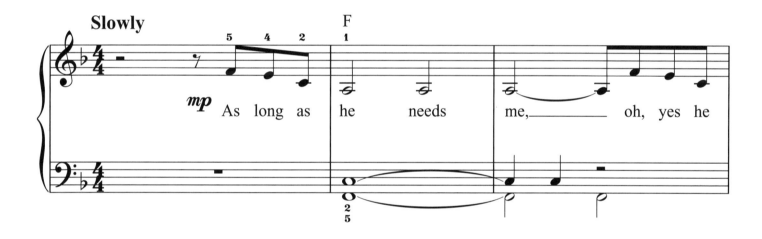

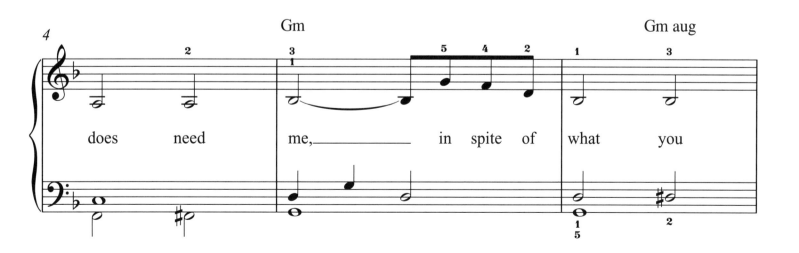

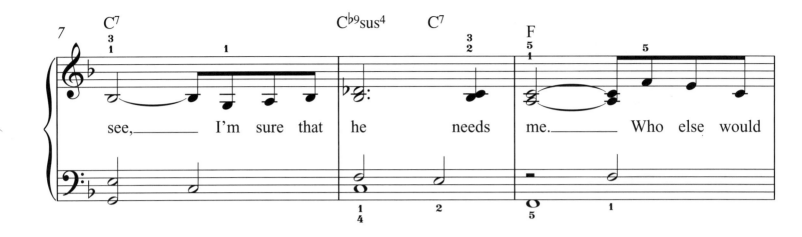

see,_____ I'm sure that he needs me._____ Who else would

love him still,_____ when they've been used so

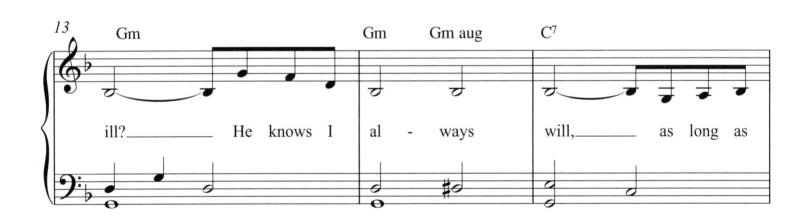

ill?_____ He knows I al - ways will,_____ as long as

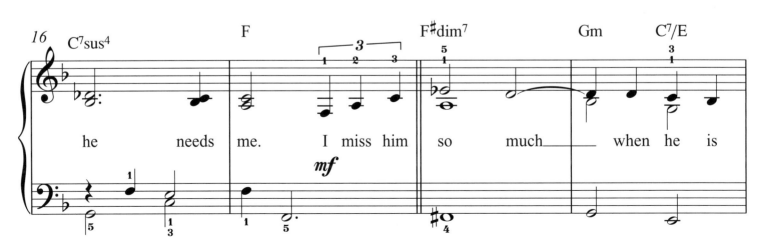

he needs me. I miss him so much_____ when he is

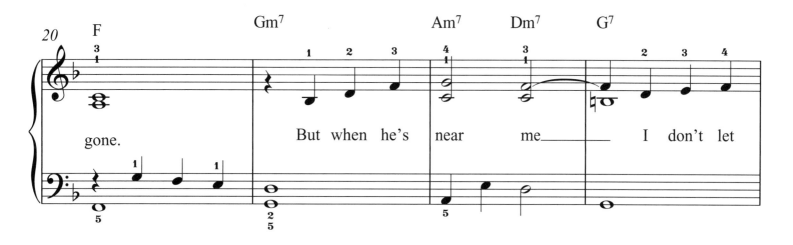

gone. But when he's near me____ I don't let

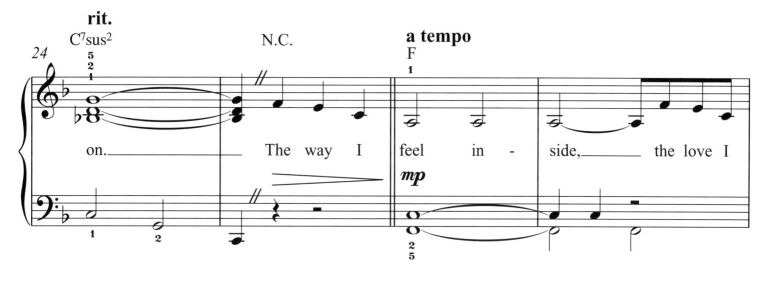

rit. **a tempo**

on.____ The way I feel in - side,____ the love I

mp

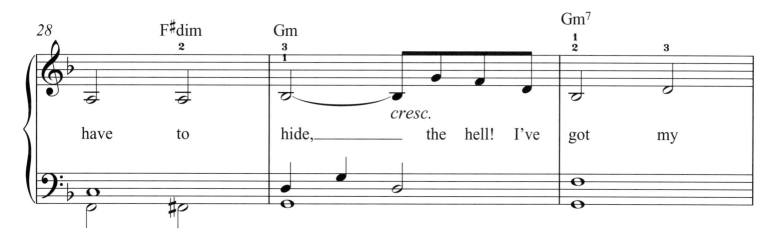

have to hide,____ the hell! I've got my

cresc.

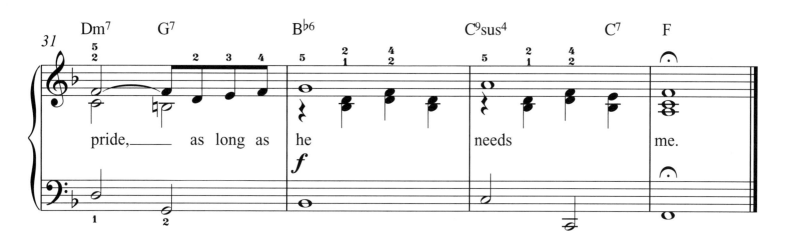

pride,____ as long as he needs me.

f

SONG & DANCE (1979)

Tell Me On A Sunday

Music by Andrew Lloyd Webber
Lyrics by Don Black

Tell Me On A Sunday was originally written in 1979 as a one-woman song-cycle. It was subsequently re-worked, however, to form the opening half of a new production entitled Song & Dance, the second half of which is a ballet based around Andrew Lloyd Webber's Variations on a Theme by Paganini.

N.B. In bar 10, the right hand takes over some of the notes in the bass clef. Follow the fingerings shown.

Use these chord diagrams as a guide:

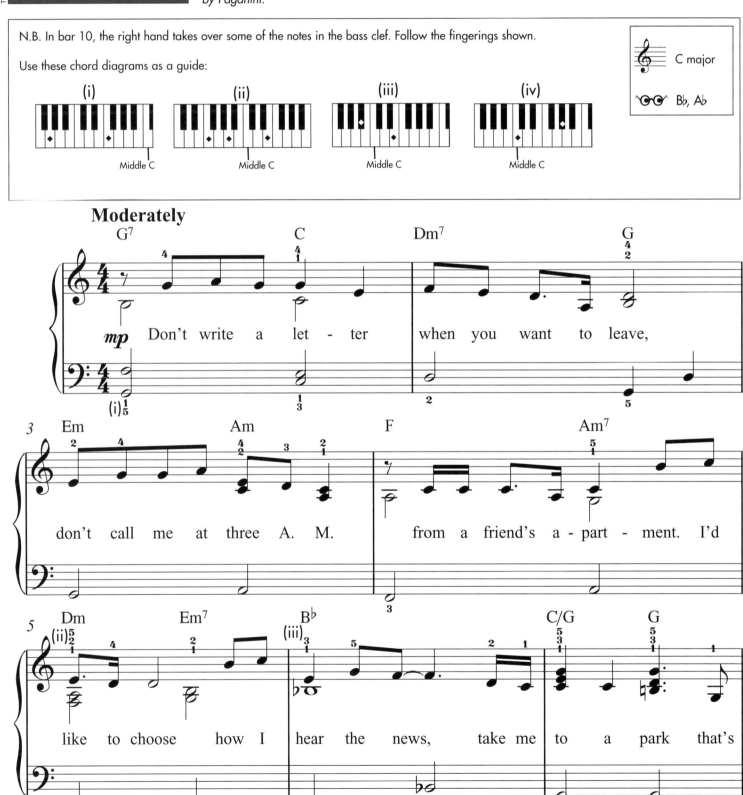

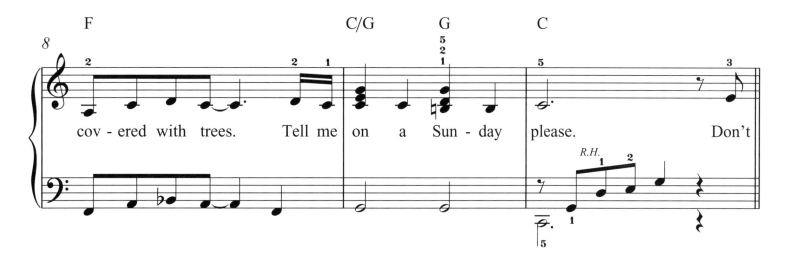

cov - ered with trees.   Tell me   on   a   Sun - day   please.   Don't

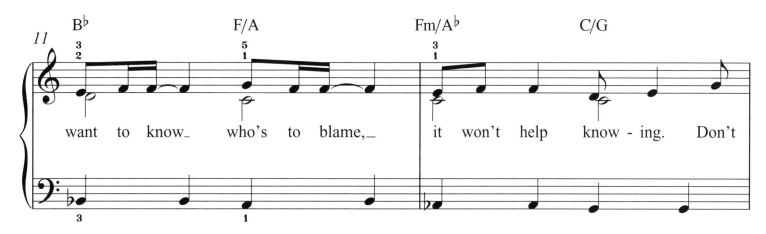

want   to   know   who's   to   blame,   it   won't   help   know - ing.   Don't

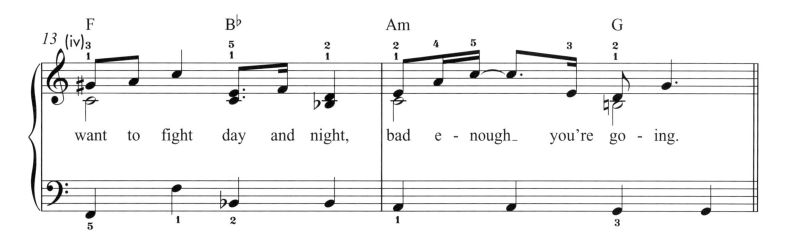

want   to   fight   day   and   night,   bad   e - nough   you're   go - ing.

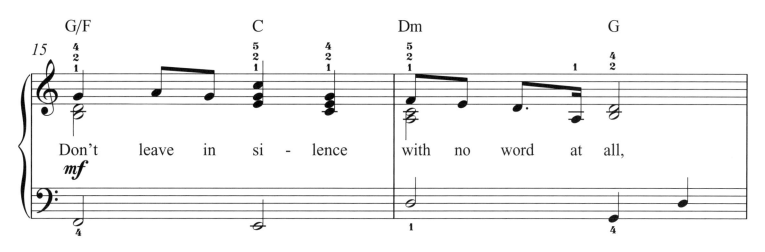

Don't   leave   in   si - lence   with   no   word   at   all,

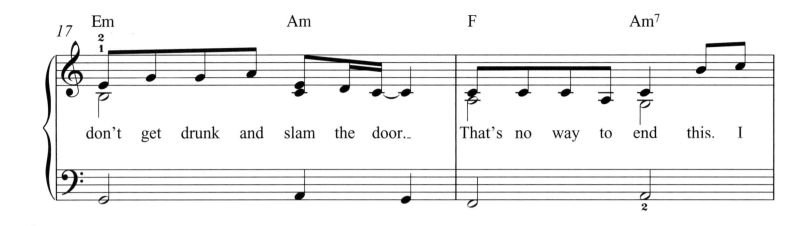

don't get drunk and slam the door.. That's no way to end this. I

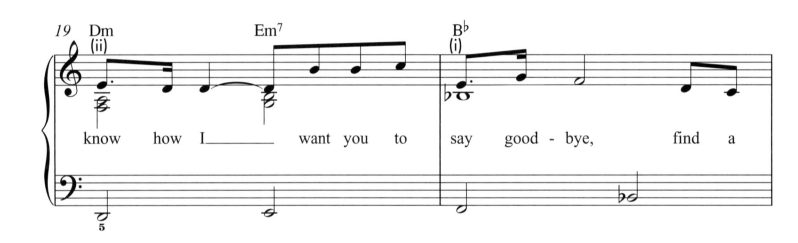

know how I_____ want you to say good - bye, find a

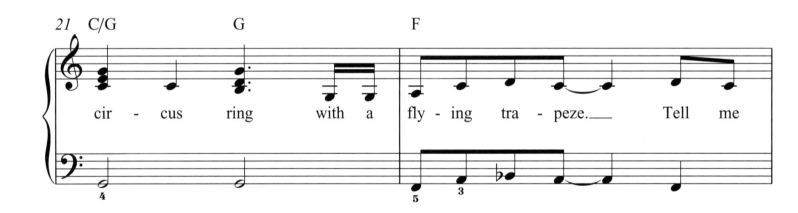

cir - cus ring with a fly - ing tra - peze.___ Tell me

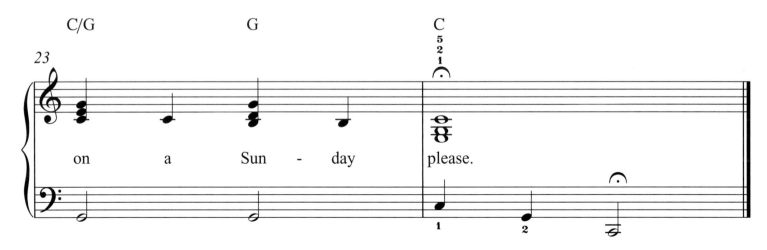

on a Sun - day please.

CATS (1981)

Memory

Music by Andrew Lloyd Webber
Lyrics by Trevor Nunn after T.S. Eliot

Andrew Lloyd Webber's musical adaptation of T.S. Eliot's Old Possum's Book Of Practical Cats first opened in London's West End in May 1981 and was an overnight success. In the 1990s Cats became the longest running musical in West End and Broadway history. The haunting melody of 'Memory' is sung by Grizabella: The Glamour Cat, a role played most famously by Elaine Page.

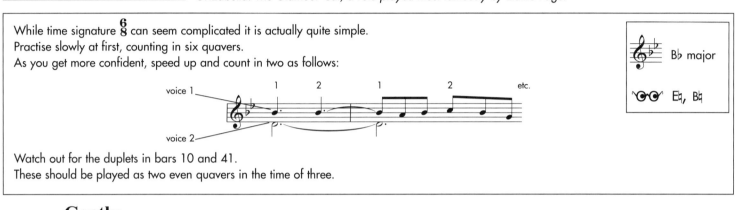

While time signature $\frac{6}{8}$ can seem complicated it is actually quite simple.

Practise slowly at first, counting in six quavers.

As you get more confident, speed up and count in two as follows:

Watch out for the duplets in bars 10 and 41.

These should be played as two even quavers in the time of three.

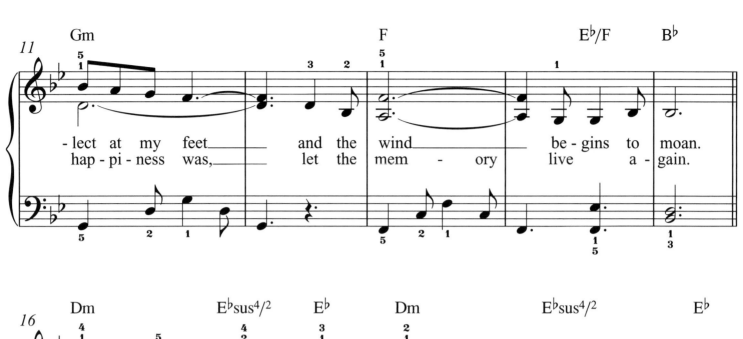

-lect at my feet_____ and the wind_____ be-gins to moan.
hap-pi-ness was,_____ let the mem - ory live a - gain.

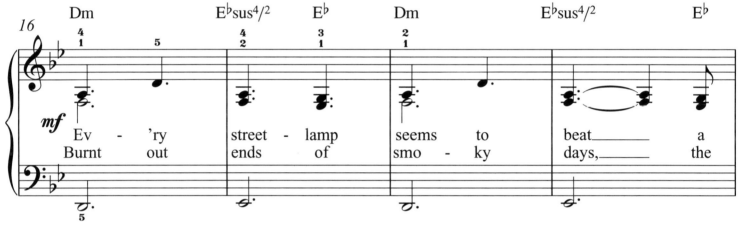

Ev - 'ry street - lamp seems to beat_____ a
Burnt out ends of smo - ky days,_____ the

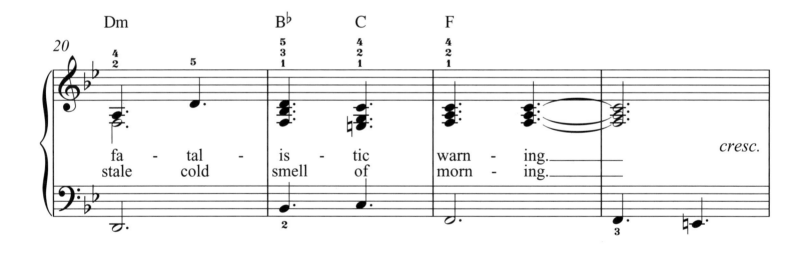

fa - tal - is - tic warn - ing._____
stale cold smell of morn - ing._____

cresc.

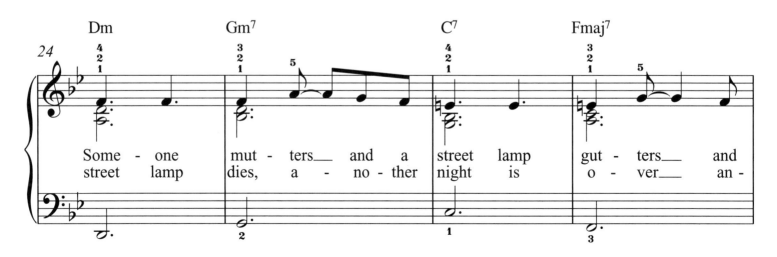

Some - one mut - ters_____ and a street lamp gut - ters_____ and
street lamp dies, a - no - ther night is o - ver_____ an -

FIDDLER ON THE ROOF (1965)

If I Were A Rich Man

Words by Sheldon Harnick
Music by Jerry Bock

Set in the small Russian village of Anatevken in the early 20th Century, Jewish father Tevye attempts (with the help of Yente, the matchmaker) to find husbands for his three eldest daughters. The daughters break with tradition and refuse their father's choice, marrying men that they love. Forced out by Russian Antisemites, Tevye and his family go in search of a better life in a new land.

As this piece is written in the style of a Russian folk dance, it contains lots of chromatic notes and modulates occasionally from major to minor.
Watch out for all the accidentals that appear throughout.

Use these chord diagrams as a guide:

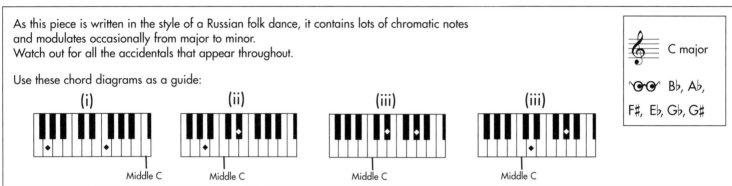

Moderate lilt

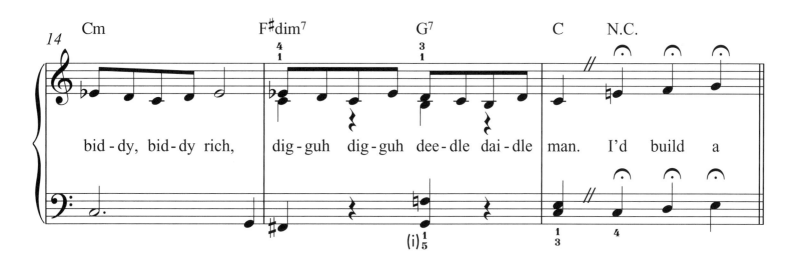

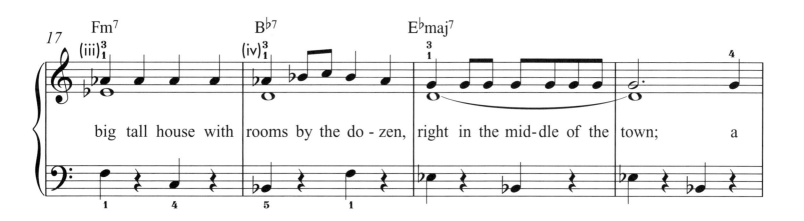

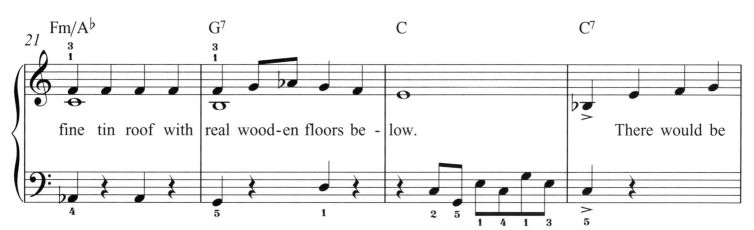

23

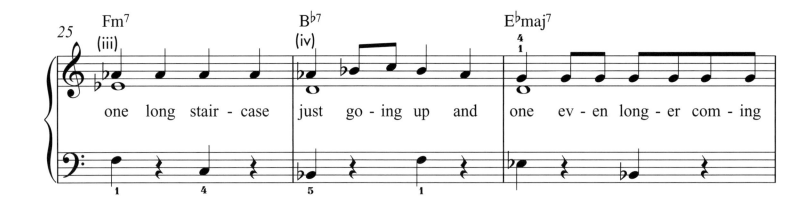

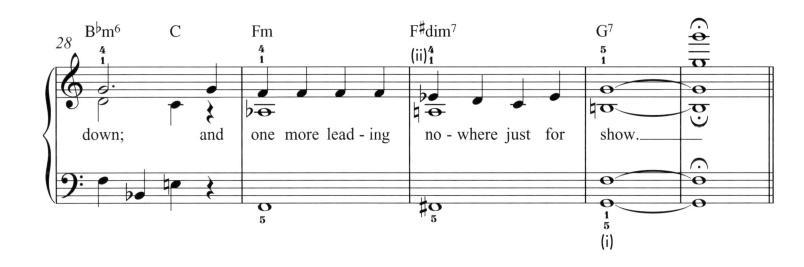

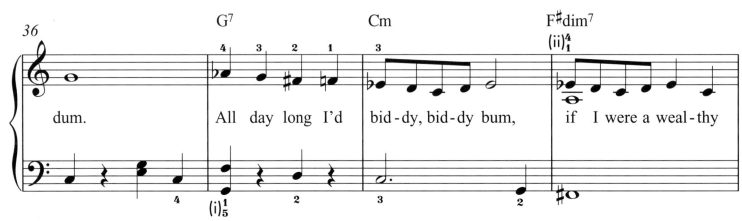

24

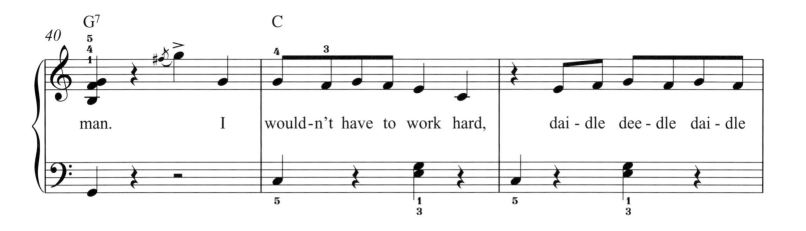

man.   I   would-n't have to work hard,   dai - dle dee - dle dai - dle

dig - guh dig - guh dee - dle dai - dle   dum.   Lord who made the

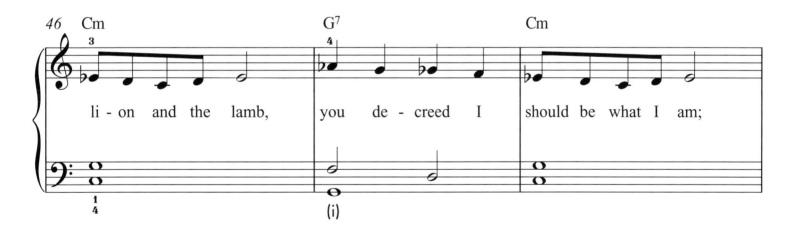

li - on and the lamb,   you de - creed I   should be what I am;

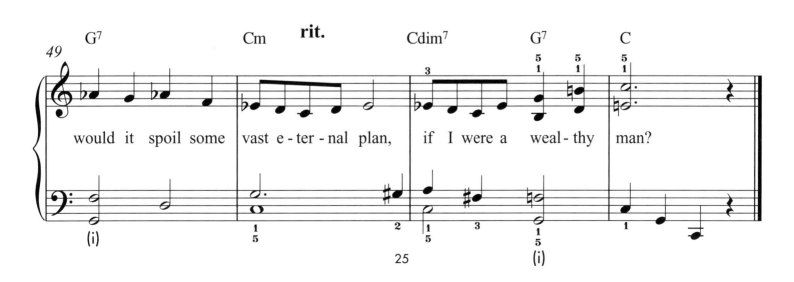

would it spoil some   vast e - ter - nal plan,   if I were a   weal - thy   man?

25

THE PHANTOM OF THE OPERA (1986)

The Music Of The Night

Music by Andrew Lloyd Webber
Lyrics by Charles Hart. Additional Lyrics by Richard Stilgoe

Based on the gothic novel Le Fantome de L'Opera by French author Gaston Leroux, Andrew Lloyd Webber's stage musical opened in London's West End in 1986 and has become one of the most popular shows of all time. 'The Music Of The Night' has been recorded by many artists including Michael Crawford, José Carreras and Barbra Streisand.

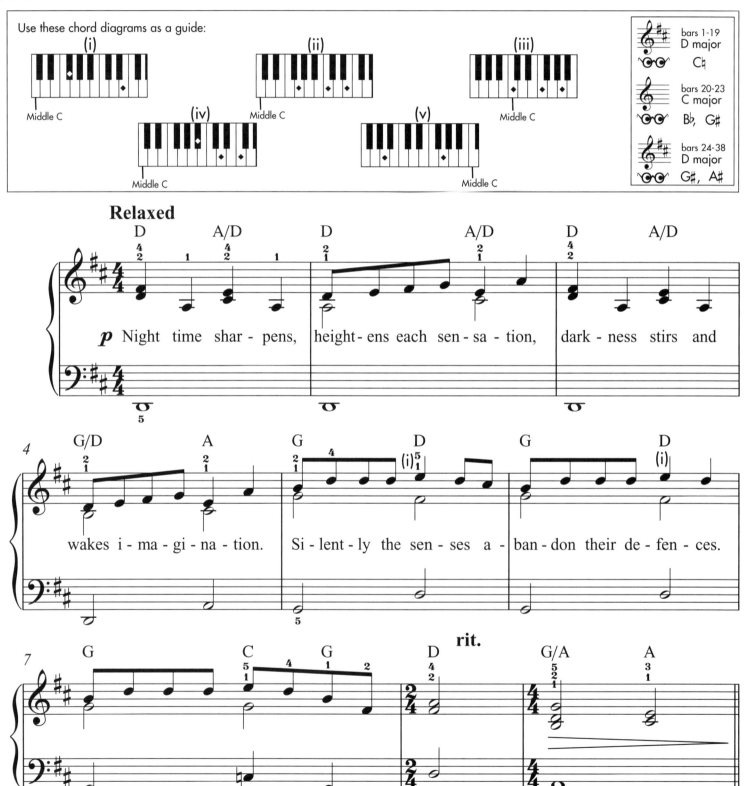

soul take you where you want to be! On - ly then will you be - long to

me. Float - ing, fall - ing, sweet in - tox - i - ca - tion.

Touch me, trust me, sa - vour each sen - sa - tion. Let the dream be - gin, let your

dark - er side give in to the po - wer of the mu - sic that I write, the

po - wer of the mu - sic of the night.

LES MISÉRABLES (1980)

Do You Hear The People Sing?

Music by Claude-Michel Schönberg
Original Lyrics by Alain Boublil & Jean-Marc Natel
English Lyrics by Herbert Kretzmer

Originally in French, Les Misérables opened at the Palais des Sports in Paris in 1980. Now shown in over 213 cities worldwide, Les Misérables remains one of the most well-loved shows.

Practise the left hand slowly on its own until you are familiar with the chord shapes in each bar - then add the right hand.

The right hand is largely made up of dotted rhythms followed by triplets.

This diagram shows how both the dotted and triplet rhythms should be fitted around a straight quaver pair:

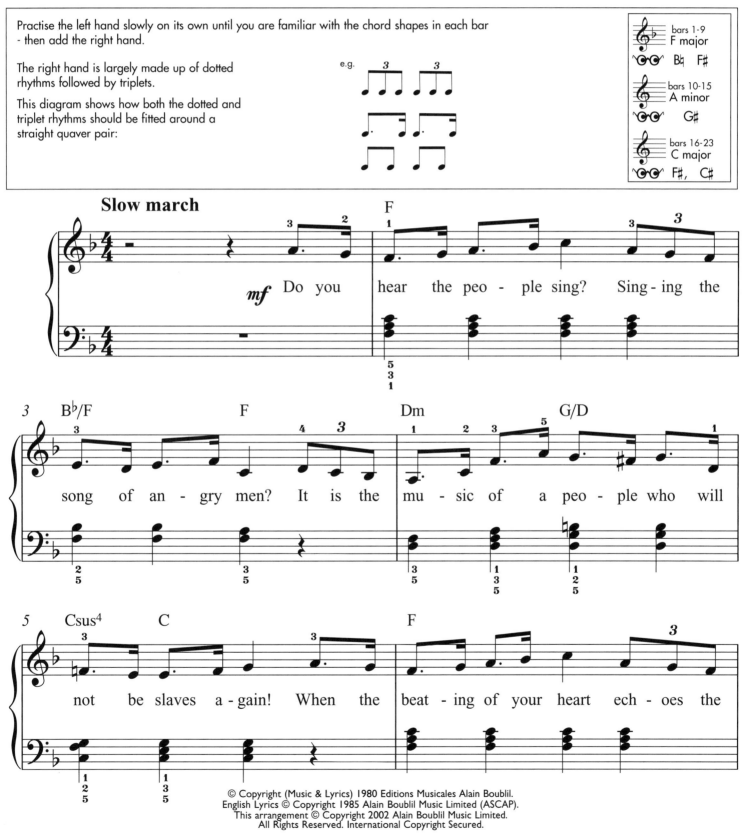

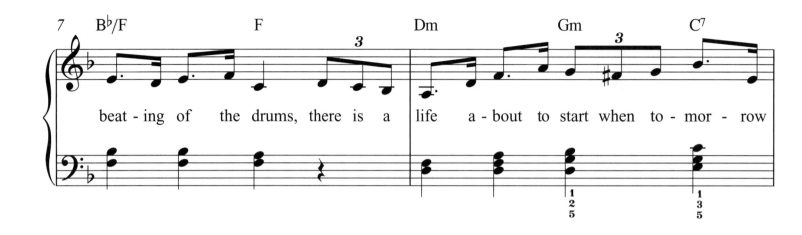

7 B♭/F   F   Dm   Gm   C⁷

beat - ing of the drums, there is a life a - bout to start when to - mor - row

9 F   Am

comes! Will you join in our cru - sade? Who will be

11 Em   Dm

strong and stand with me? Be - yond the bar - ri - cade is there a

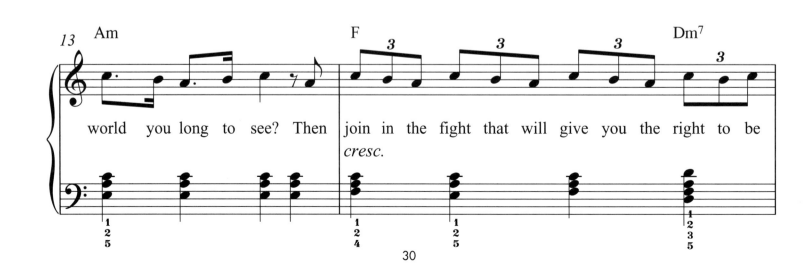

13 Am   F   Dm⁷

world you long to see? Then join in the fight that will give you the right to be

cresc.

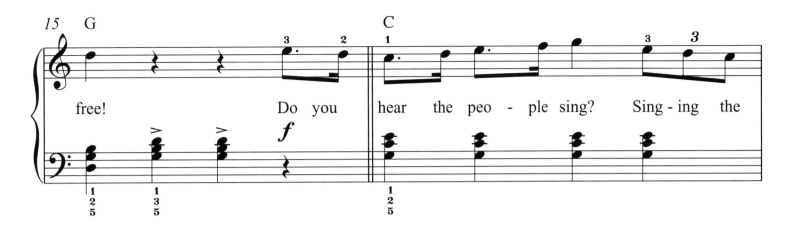

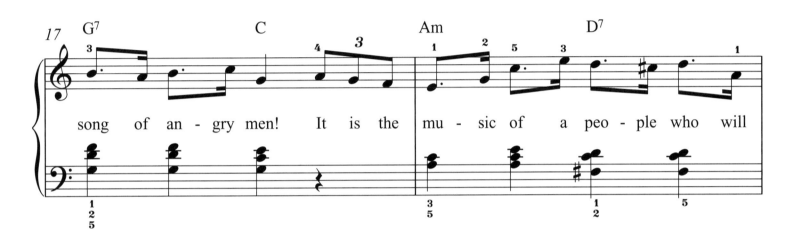

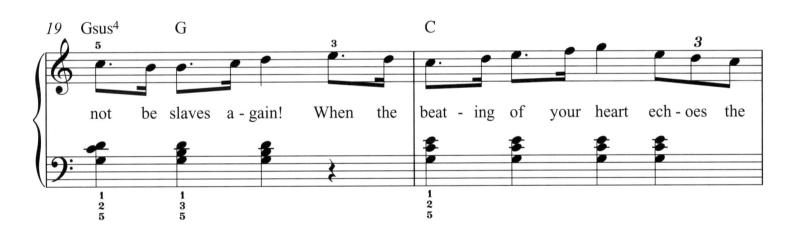

GUYS AND DOLLS (1950)

Sit Down, You're Rockin' The Boat

Words & Music by Frank Loesser

Guys And Dolls depicts a colourful picture of New York in the 1920s, with a veritable mixing pot of drunks, gamblers, nightclub entertainers, eccentrics, non-conformists and Salvation Army mission-workers. Samuel Goldwyn's 1955 movie adaptation of the Broadway smash starred Marlon Brando as Sky Masterson (shown here), Jean Simmons as Sarah Brown and Frank Sinatra as Nathan Detroit.

Between bars 9-24 the right hand has some synchopated rhythms.

For example, in bars 9-10, the word 'down' is anticipated before the first beat of the bar:

peo - ple all said "Sit down,___

A minor/ C major

Bb, Eb, G#, Ab, Gb

To fit these synchopated rhythms around the steady pulse, break each bar down into eight quavers and practise very slowly before speeding up.

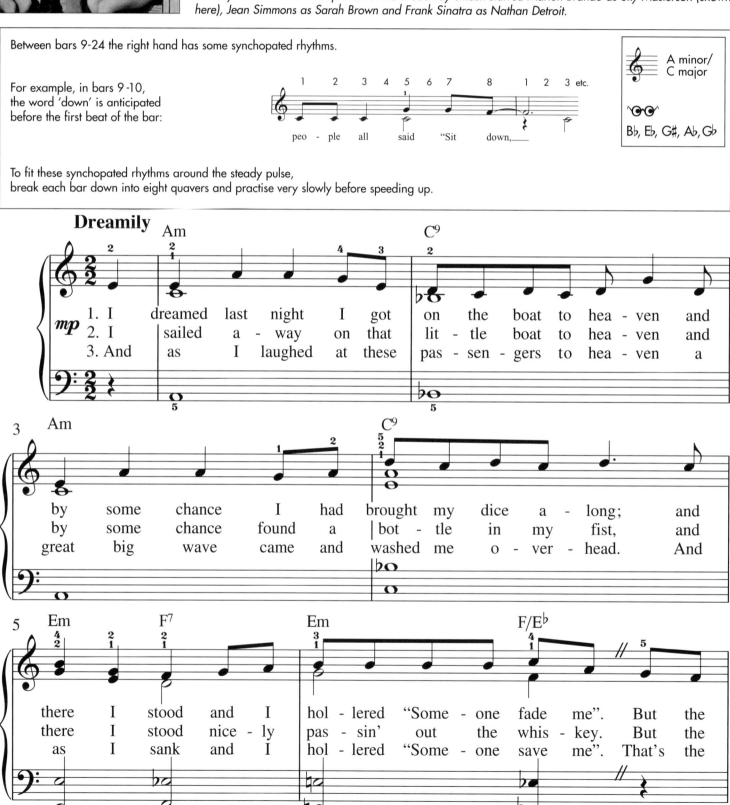

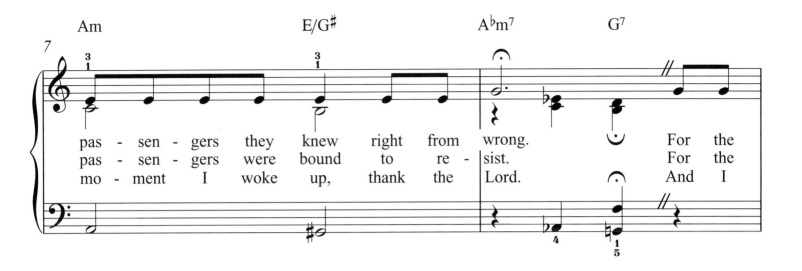

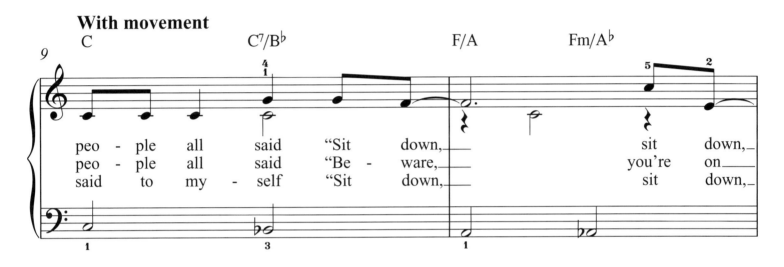

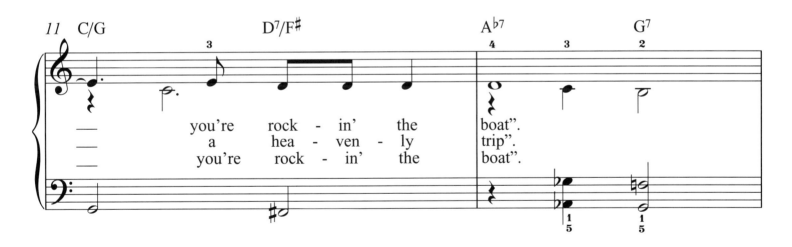

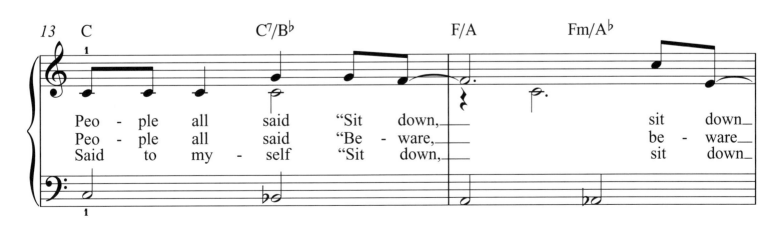

THE MUSIC MAN (1957)

Till There Was You

Words & Music by Meredith Willson

Meredith Willson's The Music Man *became a musical phenomenon, winning the 1957 Tony award for Best Musical over Leonard Bernstein's* West Side Story. *The 1962 movie starred Robert Preston as Harold Hill and Shirley Jones as Marian Paroo (pictured here). 'Till There Was You' was famously covered by The Beatles on their 1963 album* With The Beatles.

There are some tricky 7th stretches in this piece.
Use these diagrams as a guide to help you with some of them:

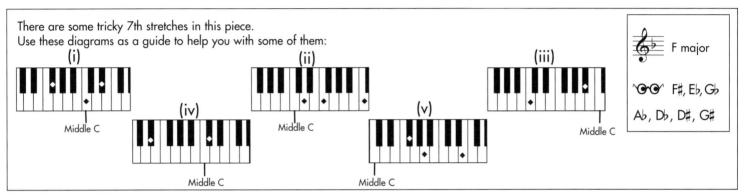

birds   in the   sky,   but I   nev - er   saw   them

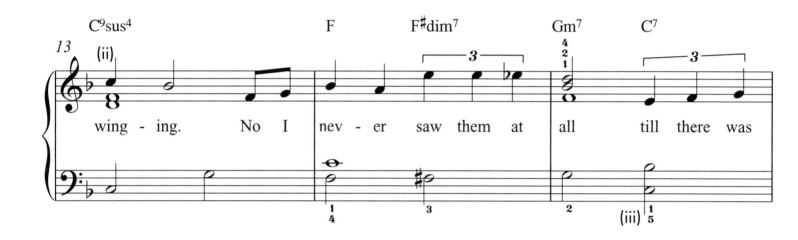

wing - ing.   No   I   nev - er   saw   them   at   all   till   there   was

you._____   And   there   was   mu - sic   and
cresc.   *mf*

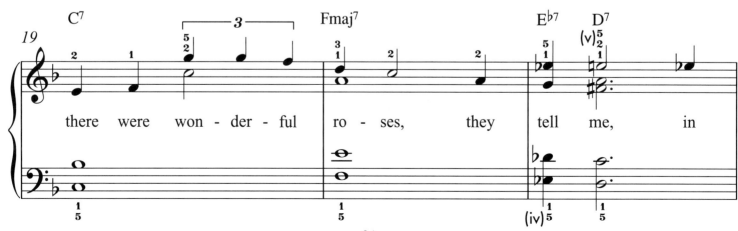

there   were   won - der - ful   ro - ses,   they   tell   me,   in

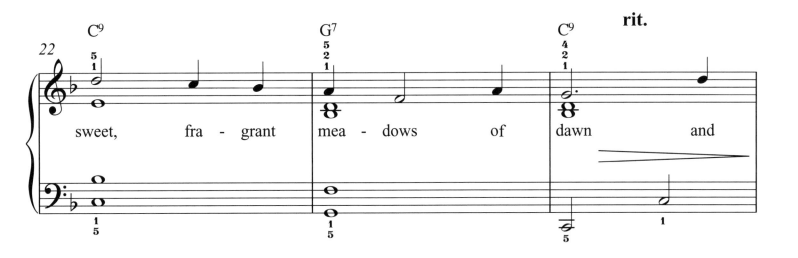

sweet,   fra - grant   mea - dows   of   dawn   and

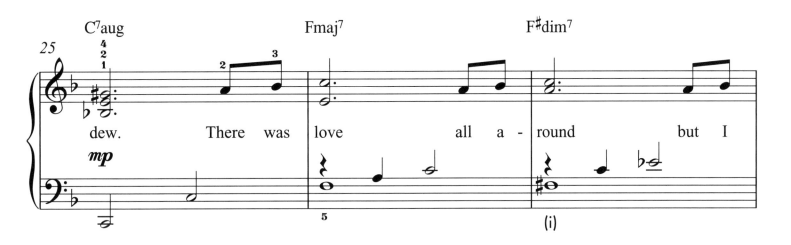

dew.   There   was   love   all   a - round   but   I

nev - er   heard   it   sing - ing.   No,   I   nev - er   heard   it   at

all   till   there   was   you.

THE SOUND OF MUSIC (1959)

Edelweiss

Words & Music by Oscar Hammerstein II & Richard Rodgers

Possibly Rodgers & Hammerstein's most popular musical, The Sound Of Music is based upon the true story of the Trapp Family Singers. Set in Austria during the Nazi occupation, Julie Andrews (pictured here in the 1965 movie) starred as a young nun Maria who becomes governess to the seven children of Captain Von Trapp. The family's musical peformances provide them with a unique opportunity to escape over the Alps to freedom in Switzerland.

Again, the little finger in the right hand often acts as an anchor, i.e. it is held down while the second voice maintains the pulse:

Practise the melody in voice 1 on its own following the fingering suggestions provided. When you have learned the melody, add the second voice.

C major

F♯, B♭, A♭

You might find it useful to use the sustain pedal on the first beat of each bar; the pedal will help hold the long note while allowing you to lift your hand to play the notes in voice 2.

Hello Dolly

Words & Music by Jerry Herman

Based on The Matchmaker by Thornton Wilder, Hello Dolly tells the tale of Mrs Dolly Levi's attempt to marry the wealthy Horace Vendergelder, whilst match-making various other couples in the process. American icon Barbra Streisand (pictured here) starred as Dolly Levi in the 1969 movie alongside Walter Matthau and Michael Crawford. The film was directed by Gene Kelly and included a cameo appearance by Louis Armstrong.

Use these chord diagrams as a guide:

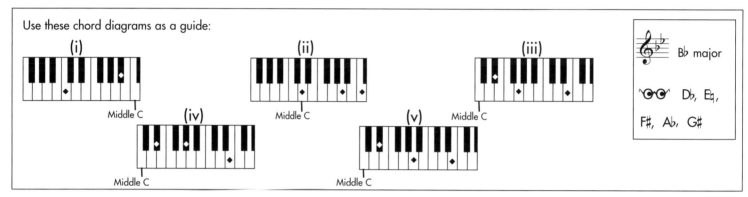

Medium strut

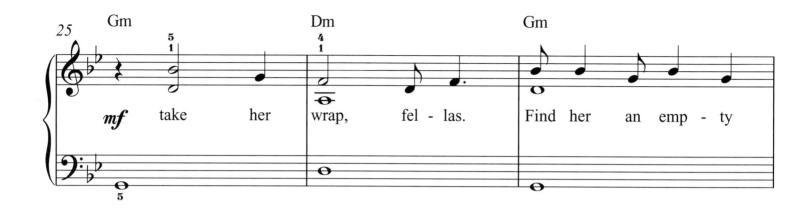

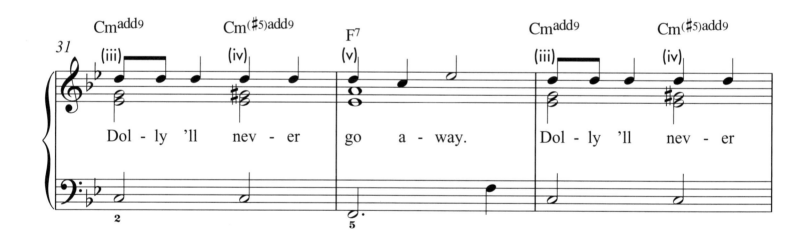

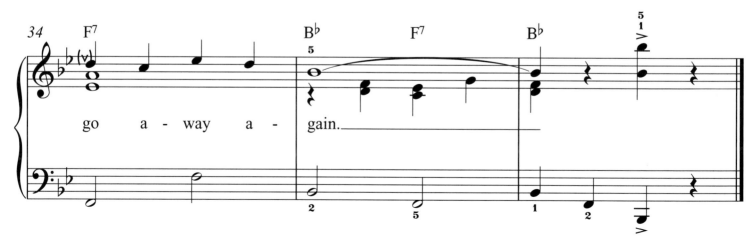

CABARET (1966)

Maybe This Time

Words & Music by Fred Ebb & John Kander

Ebb & Kander's hit musical Cabaret is based upon Christopher Isherwood's Goodbye To Berlin. Set in a seedy cabaret club, the story reveals the steady conversion of German society towards Nazism. In 1972 Bob Fosse's movie adaptation of Cabaret won an impressive eight Oscars, including that of Best Actress for Liza Minnelli in her role as Sally Bowles (pictured here).

The adjacent triplet quavers and triplet crotchets in this piece can be confusing. Take care to distinguish between the two:

You don't have to be too strict with the rhythms in the right hand melody.
As the first beat of the triplet quavers is often a rest, a *rubato* effect is produced: i.e. the melody can be pulled around in a relaxed fashion.

N.B. Keep the left hand crotchets steady throughout.

C major

G♯, B♭, C♯, E♭, F♯, A♯, D♯

Slowly

May-be this time. I'll be luck-y. May-be this time he'll stay. May-be this time, for the first time, love won't hur-ry a - way. He will hold me

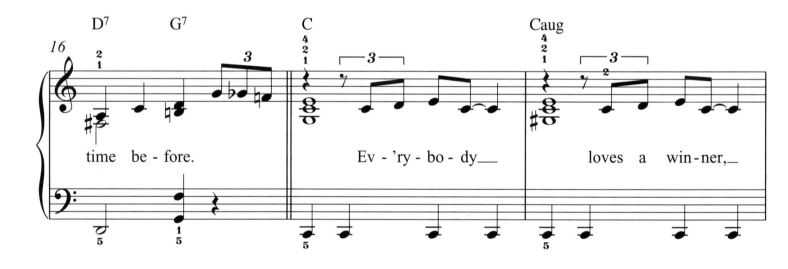

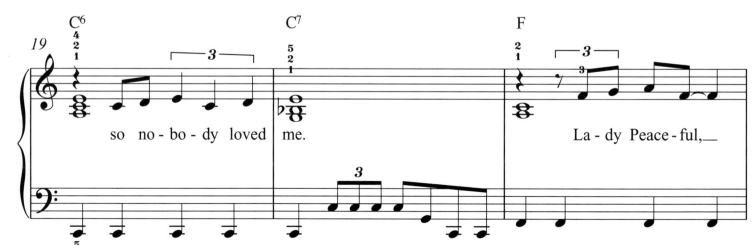

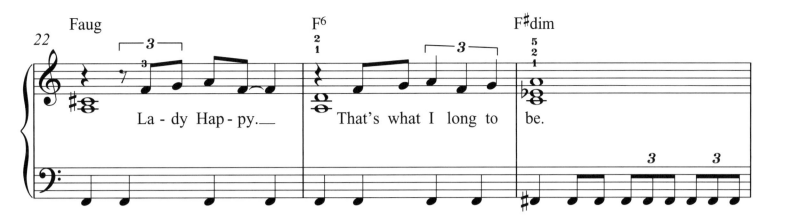

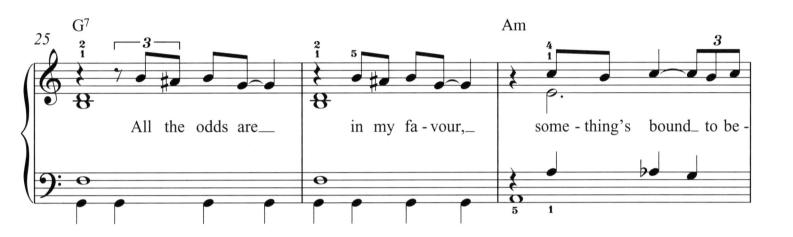

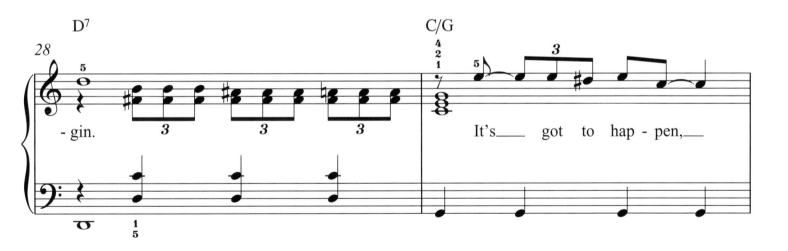

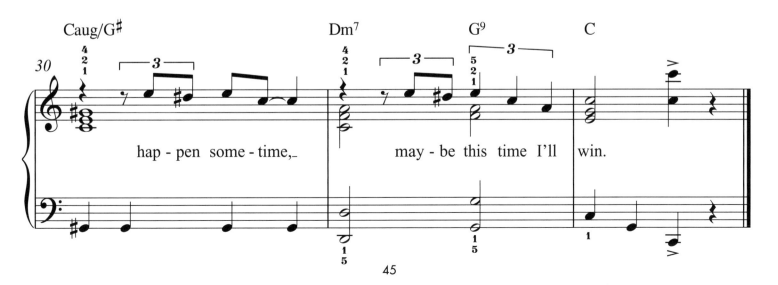

ASPECTS OF LOVE (1989)

Love Changes Everything

Music by Andrew Lloyd Webber
Lyrics by Don Black & Charles Hart

Aspects Of Love is based upon a novella of the same name by David Garnett. The show opened in the West End in 1989 and on Broadway the following year. 'Love Changes Everything', performed by Welsh tenor Michael Ball, climbed to No. 2 in the British charts in January 1989.

This piece contains lots of sixth chords in the right hand.
To help accustom your hand to the sixth position, try practising this exercise, slowly at first, then speeding up:
You could reverse the exercise so that you descend the scale, or try practising the same exercise in different keys.

G major

F♮

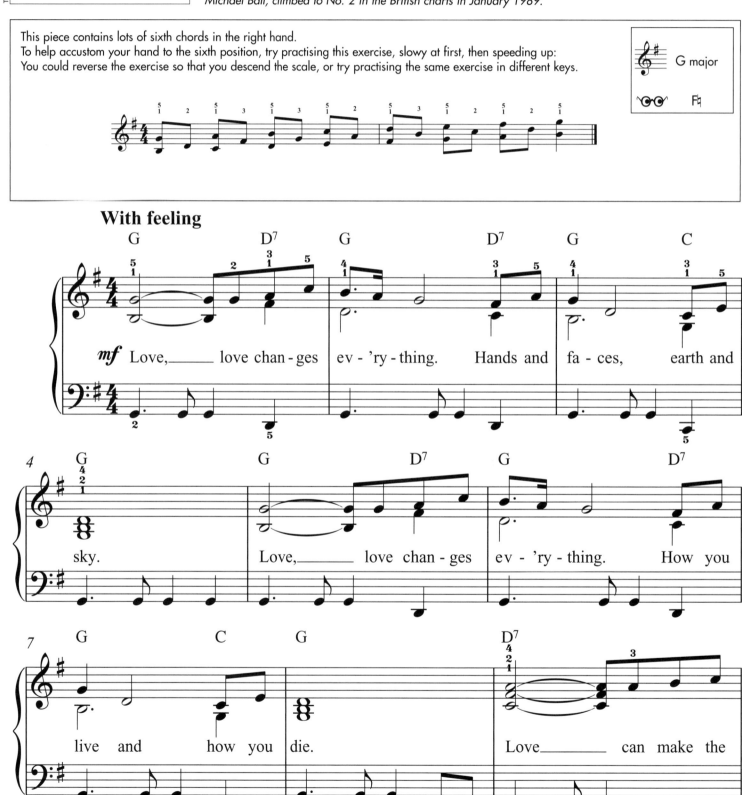

ME & MY GIRL (1937)

The Lambeth Walk

Words by Douglas Furber & Arthur Rose
Music by Noel Gay

Me & My Girl opened at the Victoria Palace Theatre in London in 1937 and ran for two years before falling into obscurity. In the 1980s it was revived by Noel Gay's son, Producer Richard Armitage, who spent years trying to track down some of his father's original score. The show tells of happy-go-lucky cockney Bill Snibson who learns he's the only heir to an earl's fortune. The only catch is that in order to get the money he has to convince a group of aristocratic executives that he is a true gentleman.

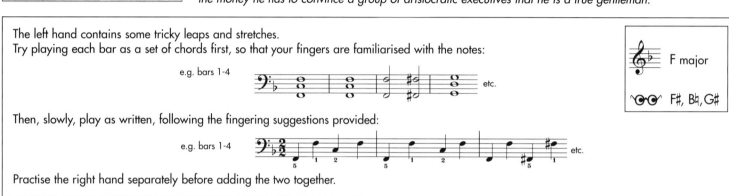

The left hand contains some tricky leaps and stretches.
Try playing each bar as a set of chords first, so that your fingers are familiarised with the notes:

e.g. bars 1-4

Then, slowly, play as written, following the fingering suggestions provided:

e.g. bars 1-4

Practise the right hand separately before adding the two together.

F major

F#, B♮, G#

With bounce

A - ny time you're Lam-beth way,__ a - ny eve - ning, a - ny day,__

you'll find us all do - in' the Lam - beth walk.

Ev - 'ry lit - tle Lam-beth girl,__ with her lit - tle Lam-beth pal__

ROBERTA (1933)

Smoke Gets In Your Eyes

Words & Music by Otto Harbach & Jerome Kern

Harbach & Kern's Roberta is based on the novel Gowns By Roberta by Alice Duer Miller.
In 1965 the show was made into a movie, adapted especially to incorporate the dancing skills of Fred Astaire and Ginger Rogers (pictured here). Although the pair played secondary roles to the leads (played by Irene Dunne & Randlph Scott) their routines are one of the film's highlights.

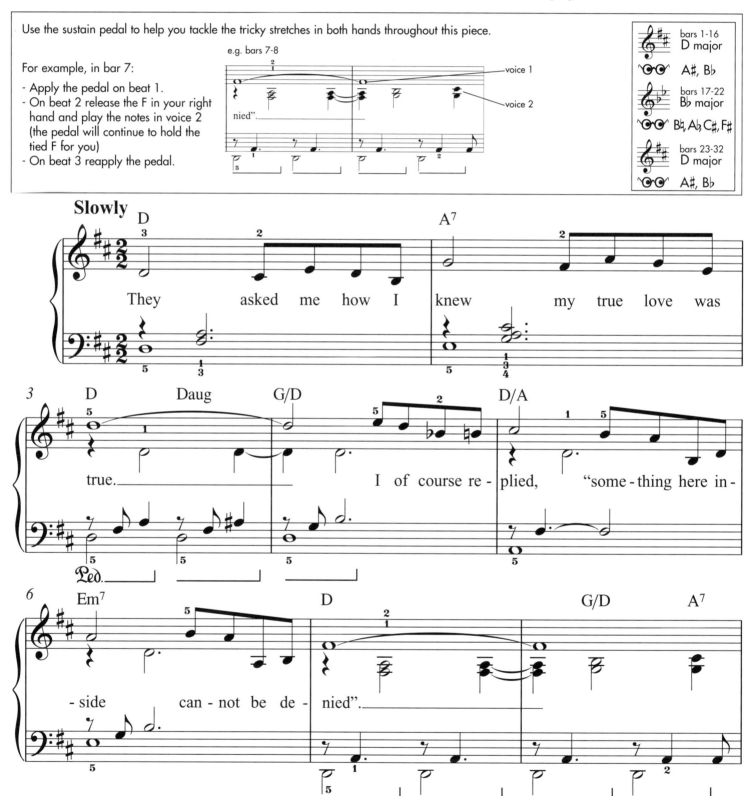

Use the sustain pedal to help you tackle the tricky stretches in both hands throughout this piece.

For example, in bar 7:

- Apply the pedal on beat 1.
- On beat 2 release the F in your right hand and play the notes in voice 2 (the pedal will continue to hold the tied F for you)
- On beat 3 reapply the pedal.

Lyrics:

They asked me how I knew my true love was true. I of course re-plied, "some-thing here in-side can-not be de-nied".

They said "Some day you'll find, all who love are blind.

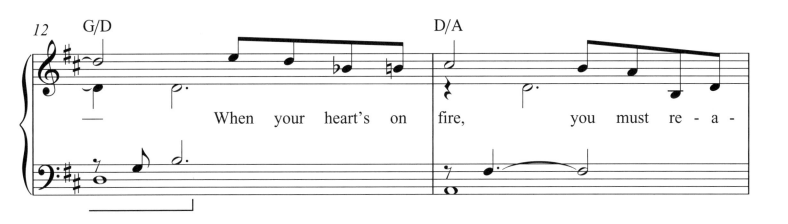

When your heart's on fire, you must re-a-

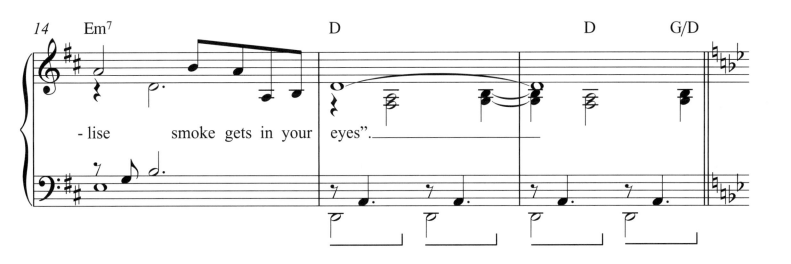

-lise smoke gets in your eyes".

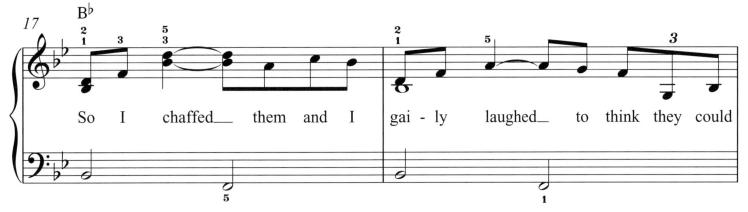

So I chaffed____ them and I gai-ly laughed____ to think they could

SWEET CHARITY (1966)

Big Spender

Words by Dorothy Fields
Music by Cy Coleman

Shirley McClaine (pictured here) starred as Charity Hope Valentine in the 1969 movie of Coleman & Fields'
Sweet Charity directed by Bob Fosse. The musical depicts the misadventures of Charity, who always gives
her heart to the wrong man. 'Big Spender', the show's most famous song, was a huge hit for Dame Shirley
Bassey.

Use these chord diagrams as a guide:

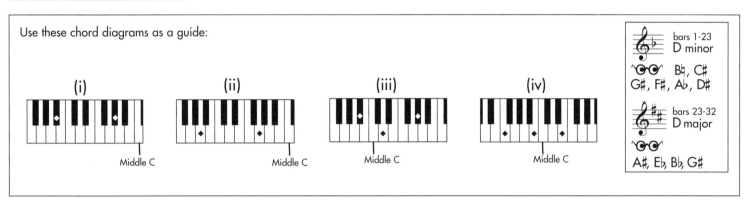

Glossary Of Symbols & Terms

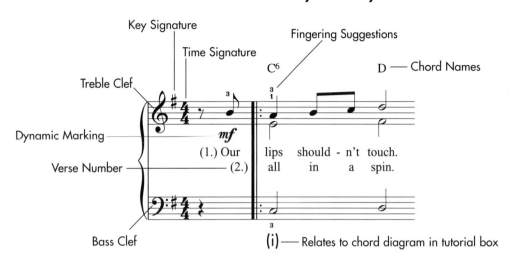

Key Signature
Time Signature
Fingering Suggestions
Treble Clef
C⁶
D — Chord Names
Dynamic Marking
Verse Number
Bass Clef
(1.) Our   lips   should - n't touch.
(2.)   all   in   a   spin.
(i) — Relates to chord diagram in tutorial box

Each piece is accompanied by this box which highlights the *key signature,* as well as any *accidentals* in the order in which they appear in the music:

KEY

A maj

C♮

Watch out for

Symbols

Tie — When two similar notes are tied together, the value of each note is added together. So, the value of the tied notes in this example is six crotchet beats.

Slur — A slur over a group of notes indicates that they should be played as a smooth phrase. N.B. A slur occurs above or below a series of *different* notes, while a tie is always placed next to similar notes (see above).

Dots above or below notes indicate they should be played *Staccato,* i.e. short and crisp.

This symbol indicates the notes should be played *Sforzando,* i.e. heavily accented.

p = *piano* (quiet)

mp = *mezzopiano* (moderately quiet)

pp = *pianissimo* (very quiet)

f = *forte* (loud)

mf = *mezzoforte* (moderately loud)

ff = *fortissino* (very loud)

 = *diminuendo* (get quieter)

 = *crescendo* (get louder)

⌒ = *pause* (note is held on for longer than its value)

‖: = start repeat   :‖ = end repeat   8va- - - - - ⌐ Indicates music to be played an octave higher than written.

R.H. = Right Hand   L.H. = Left Hand

8vb- - -⌐ Indicates music to be played an octave lower than written.

│1. ┐ On the *first* time of playing, follow this bar.

│2. ─ On the *second* time of playing, follow this bar.

Terms

Andante = at a steady, walking pace

rit. = *ritenuto,* meaning to slow down gradually

rall. = *rallentando,* meaning to slow down gradually

a tempo = return to the original speed suggested at the start of a section

N.C. = no chord

⊕ Coda = indicates start of Coda section

To ⊕ Coda = jump to the start of the Coda section

D.S. al Coda = go back to the sign 𝄋 and play through to until you reach

FINE = the end

Chromatic = notes which don't belong in the piece's key, but appear as accidentals

Modulates = changes in key

Synchopated = weaker beats are accented so as to suggest a change in time signature

Rubato = strict time is disregarded and the beats can be pulled around, emphasising important stresses in the lyrics